your dog
A LIFETIME
RECORD

EUKANUBA

An informative and entertaining activity book

for dog lovers.

This is an activity book. Although it is full of useful information and practical tips, it is not just for reading: this book wants to be used!

Record all those precious moments and add your favourite pictures. Make notes about your dog's growth, health and training. Fill in questions and charts. Check his nutritional needs, and of course, use the money off coupons! Your dog is like no other. So he certainly deserves a book that's like no other book. Enjoy your dog, enjoy completing his own book.

let's begin
AT THE
BEGINNING

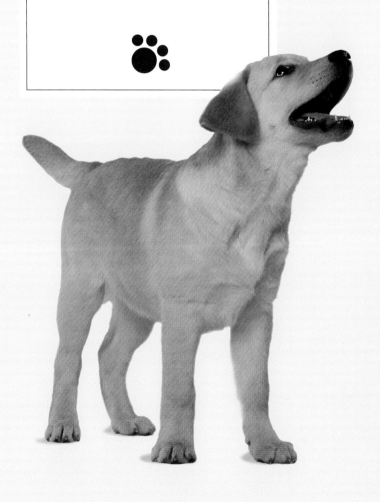

No. 0 0 3 5 4 0 7 6 2 0 1 8

☎ Telephone number of veterinary surgeon:

☎ Telephone number of pet insurance company:

1 | Full name:

2 | Pet name:

3 | Sex:

4 | Date of birth:

5 | Place of birth:

6 | Colour (eyes and coat):

7 | Distinguishing Markings:

8 | Vaccinations:

Outline your dog's paw in here.

TIPS TIPS TIPS TIPS TIPS TIPS TIPS TIPS TIPS TIPS

Keep this data at hand, for whenever you need to call the vet.

Medical record

Vaccinations	Puppy	Booster	Repeat-injections	
Date				
Illnesses	date	type		
Treatment	date	type		

Affix a photo in here.

This is my family.

Name of dam

Name of sire

Grandmother

Grandfather

Grandmother

Grandfather

Breed

the start of
A NEW
LIFE

The start of a new life.
When you bring a puppy into your home for the first time, he'll probably feel frightened and apprehensive. After all, he is in a strange new environment. You may comfort him by holding him as shown, with one hand under his chest and the other supporting his

hind legs. By holding him in this way he will feel secure and protected.

His own place.
Your puppy needs a place of his own. Give him a box or a dog bed inside a pen - in a warm, draught-free corner. Putting a box on its side to make an enclosed bed will make him feel even more secure. Why? Well, a cave was home to the dog's wolf-like ancestor, so your puppy instinctively feels cosy and safe in anything remotely resembling a cave, even if its just a turned-over box. Add some warm, washable bedding (like a blanket or towel) and

your puppy's place is complete.

Naming your puppy.
Remember, when choosing a name for your puppy, two-syllable names that end in a vowel, like Tasha or Bonzo, are easiest for a dog to recall.

From bowls to brushes.
Eating and drinking bowls, preferably made from stainless steel, crockery or glass, should be placed in a quiet, out-of-the-way place. They should not be easy to tip-over and plenty of fresh water should be available at all times. To complete your dog's outfit, he should have a collar and lead with dog tag (detailing name, address and/or phone number), plus a comb and brush for grooming.

TIPS TIPS TIPS TIPS TIPS TIPS TIPS

Never send your dog to his bed because you are angry. He'll associate this place with punishment, and develop a dislike of it.

Instinctively a puppy may want to defend his food and may even try to bite you. Correct him, show him you are the boss and gradually he will come to accept this.

For larger puppies and for older dogs, a stand under their eating bowls is preferable. Don't forget the drinking bowl either!

Dear diary, my first day in my new home:

House-training: don't worry.

Many people fear that house-training a puppy is troublesome. True, it takes attention, patience and perseverance. Some dogs are more trainable than others, however it does not have to be difficult and it does not have to take a long time - as long as you stick to a few basic principles.

Elementary schooling.

Begin house-training your puppy right away.

Start by putting him on a regular feeding schedule and make frequent trips outside. The signs to look for are: your puppy walking around in

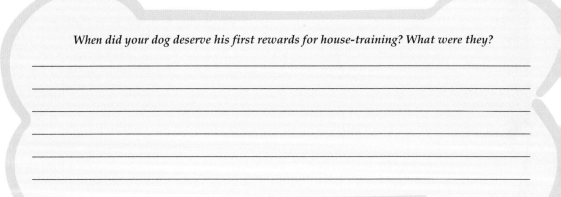

When did your dog deserve his first rewards for house-training? What were they?

_____

_____

_____

_____

_____

circles, sitting or whining at the door, or your puppy voluntarily giving you 'the look'. When you catch him in the act, immediately take him outside to finish. When he has finished relieving himself, quietly praise him and bring him back inside. Soon he will connect 'going' outdoors with praise.

Timing is the word.

The best times to take your puppy outside are first thing in the morning, just after his naps, upon returning home to

a puppy that has been left alone, just after meals and last thing in the evening.

Accidents do happen. Should you discover a mess, do not raise your voice or smack your pup. While he'll certainly cower in fear, he's too young to connect your reprimand with his mess.

Although of course, every dog has its own character and development pattern - as a rule of thumb, a three-month old puppy can be house-trained within two weeks, but a lot depends on the owner's patience and common sense.

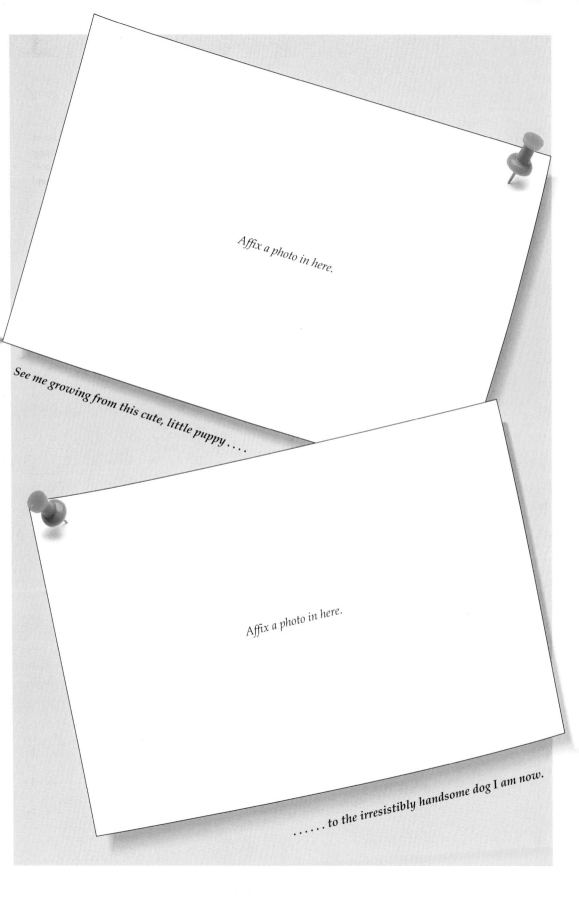

Affix a photo in here.

See me growing from this cute, little puppy . . . .

Affix a photo in here.

. . . . . . to the irresistibly handsome dog I am now.

The serious business of playing.

Puppies love playing and definitely need to play.
To them, it's not a game, it's an indispensable part of growing up. In playing, puppies train their stalking and chasing abilities and their capacities for guarding and hunting.
So it's a game, but at the same

Helping him teethe.

Puppies teethe between the ages of three and six months, and they need to chew on something to help the new teeth come through.
Help avoid accidents by giving your puppy a choice of good, indestructible objects to chew. Your pet shop will have an excellent selection.

Don't give your puppy real bones, not even to play with. These could splinter, hurt his mouth and cause choking if a sliver is swallowed.

Do not give a puppy an old shoe, or any shoe-like material to chew. Many people do, and this will make him think all shoes are acceptable for chewing. Moreover, some shoes contain potentially poisonous tanning agents.

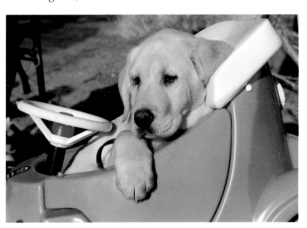

time it's serious business, too. Remember, even when your dog has grown up, he still needs you to spend a lot of time playing with him.

Watch out for choking or swallowing and make sure his toys are not too small.
Make his toy especially attractive to him by playing games with it.

Help your puppy avoid the wrong things by keeping them away from him. Especially make sure that cleansers, paint thinners, household chemicals and other harmful substances are safely out of his reach.

Affix a photo in here.

It may be a game, but I'm very serious about it!

Choice of toys.

Give your puppy his favourite toy whenever he starts to chew an unacceptable object. Say 'No' sternly, take the forbidden item away and replace it with a rubber ball or bone. When he starts to chew on his own toy, praise him for good behaviour. He'll respond happily. Not all toys are equally suitable for puppies. Rubber is suitable only when it is really solid and hard. Hide chews may be a good choice, but make sure they cannot be torn, even after prolonged chewing. Objects from which pieces can be torn should be avoided at all times.

I love it! These are my favourite toys:

FOOD FOR THOUGHT

Food for thought.

Everyone has heard about vitamins and minerals, carbohydrates and fibre, fats and proteins, but few people know the full importance of these nutrients. These pages are about food and growth, and your dog's digestive system. You'll find lots of feeding tips for healthy growth. But let's start at the very beginning.

Feeding your dog table scraps is not advisable as it provides an incomplete and unbalanced diet.

So what does your dog really need for a fully balanced diet? To understand your dog's nutritional needs, test your knowledge below.

Fats for energy.

The body's primary need is energy. Energy to maintain the body, to breathe, to run, to play and to grow. Fat is the best source of this energy. In fact, fats are a small miracle in themselves. They contain about 2.5 times more available energy than proteins or carbohydrates. Fats are essential in every dog's diet.

Fats provide and promote the assimilation of fat-soluble vitamins (A,D,E and K), protect against cold, provide protection for vulnerable organs, give a healthy coat and enhance the taste of food.

No doubt about it: he's a carnivore.

Your dog is a descendant of a large family of carnivores: wild, predatory animals surviving by eating other animals. His digestive system is very similar to that of his forefather's. This means your dog is a meat-eater, but not an animal that eats meat exclusively, although he is best fed with protein and fat from meat sources, rather than from cheaper vegetable substitutes.

Test your knowledge:

1. *Which fats are best for your dog?*
   a. *vegetable fats*
   b. *animal-based fats*
   c. *synthetic fats*

2. *Which option provides the best source(s) of protein for your dog?*
   a. *chicken and eggs*
   b. *soya*
   c. *wheat*

The right answers to the questions are 1.b and 2.a.

Building the body with proteins.

Proteins are the building blocks for muscle, bone, blood and other tissues, as well as for the immune system which helps prevent disease. They are also vital for the hormones and enzymes that keep the cellular factories going.

Proteins can be found in meat, fish, soya or wheat middlings, as well as in chicken and egg. The proteins in the latter two are highly digestible and result in small, firm stools.

Carbohydrates and fibre.

For short-term energy, ie: running and jumping,

Vitamins and minerals.

Vitamins and minerals help your dog develop his bones, teeth and coat and they protect him from disease and infection. No breed requires more or less vitamins and minerals than another. What matters is the actual daily intake. A complete and balanced food should contain all the required vitamins, minerals and trace elements, balanced to the energy content of the food. An excess of specific vitamins may even lead to problems, like skeletal diseases. Often, more health problems are created by oversupply of vitamins and minerals than by deficiencies.

Last but not least, water.

On a volume basis, water is the most important nutrient. Your dog should have an ample supply of fresh, clean water available at all times - even a small percentage loss of body water may cause your dog distress - a 15% loss of body water can be fatal.

Proteins can be broken down into amino acids. Some of these are manufactured by the body. Others, however, are termed essential amino acids, because they must be present in the daily diet. For your dog to remain healthy, his diet must contain adequate amounts of each of 10 essential amino acids in order to provide the required building blocks for growth and tissue repair.

carbohydrates are the primary source. Carbohydrates also provide fibre. Crude fibre is by definition not digestible, its function is purely mechanical. Total dietary fibre is responsible for optimal intestinal health and transit time. In other words, it functions as a bowel regulator and influences the absorption of nutrients, including water from the gut.

The need for variety is a human trait. Eukanuba dog foods are complete and balanced and contain a variety of nutritious ingredients. However, if you want to vary your dog's diet, you can mix a complete dry food with a complete canned food.

There are several Formulas of Eukanuba canned food from which to choose.
Never feed him your favourite foods as a replacement for his meals or as a reward.
Use dog biscuits if you want to reward him.

Affix a photo in here.

Feeding your puppy.

A puppy can grow as much in its first year as a human being does in the first fourteen years. So your dog's nutritional requirements may never be more demanding than when he's a young puppy. It takes a careful balance of high-quality ingredients to provide these requirements. Eukanuba Puppy and Eukanuba Junior are specially formulated for the first months of your dog's life. The special size and texture of the food have been created to make it easier for your puppy to eat. As it is so digestible, he will utilise more of the food he takes in for nourishment than with many other foods. This means optimum health and small, firm stools for easy clean up.

Dogs don't need variety.

Contrary to popular belief, dogs do not get 'tired of' or 'bored with' their food.

Rewarding my friend.

TIPS TIPS TIPS TIPS TIPS TIPS TIPS TIPS TIPS TIPS TIPS TIPS TIPS TIPS TIPS

Growing puppies have tremendous energy requirements, yet have a very small stomach capacity. Therefore rather than feed a canned food, it is better to feed them a top quality, complete, dry food.

Most dogs can change from Eukanuba Puppy to Eukanuba Junior at around 10 weeks. Eukanuba Junior - particularly for larger breeds - is the ideal food for transition between adolescence and adulthood. Afterwards they can switch over to Eukanuba adult products such as Regular, Premium or Lamb & Rice, depending on the dog's preference.

How much and when?

For a small or medium breed puppy, scheduled portion controlled feeding is recommended. This means you feed your puppy his daily ration at specified times throughout the day. For the first six months, feed 1/3 in the morning, 1/3 in the afternoon and 1/3 in the evening. After six months of age, switch to 1/2 in the morning and 1/2 in the evening.

For large or giant breeds, a portion controlled method is strongly recommended.

Alternatively, you can put your puppy's daily portion in his bowl in the morning and allow him to eat it throughout the day as his body requires nourishment.

Remember, gradual growth is essential and it is important to keep your puppy lean. Puppies that grow too fast may develop bone-defects.

In this diagram you see growth curves for several breeds and that of a child. As you can see, some breeds continue to grow longer than others. A child keeps on growing much longer. Put down a dot every month at the appropriate weight for your own dog, and connect the dots. You'll have your own dog's growth curve.

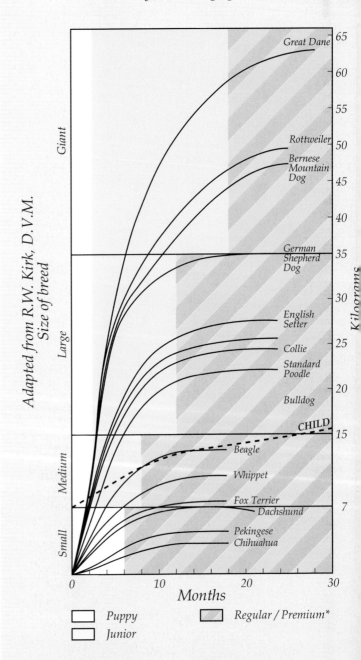

* Depending on dog's activity and preference.

Guide to adult dogs body weight (in kg).

Breed	Male	Female
Affenpinscher	4	3
Afghan Hound	27	23
Airedale Terrier	25	22
Alaskan Malamute	56	38
Basenji	11	10
Basset Hound	35	28
Beagle	14	13
Bearded Collie	28	22
Bedlington Terrier	8.5	8
Belgian Shepherd Dog	35	28
Bernese Mountain Dog	50	45
Bichon Frise	11.5	10
Bloodhound	50	45
Border Collie	25	20
Border Terrier	6.5	5.5
Borzoi	41	34
Bouvier des Flandres	40	35
Boxer	30	28
Briard	39	34
Bulldog	27	23
Bullmastiff	57	45
Bull Terrier	20.5	20.5
Cairn Terrier	7.5	6
Cavalier King Charles Spaniel	7	7
Chihuahua	3	2.5
Chow Chow	27	21
Cocker Spaniel	14	13
Corgi	11	10
Dachshund, standard	10	10
Dachshund, miniature	4.5	4.5

Breed	Male	Female
Dalmatian	27	23
Deerhound	43	33
Dobermann	37	29
English Setter	30	27
Fox Terrier	8.5	7.5
French Bulldog	15	11
German Shepherd Dog	38	32
Golden Retriever	34	30
Great Dane	54	46
Greyhound	31	24
Irish Setter	28	25
Irish Terrier	12	12
Irish Wolfhound	55	41
Italian Spinone	36.5	31.5
Jack Russell Terrier	11.5	10
Japanese Akita	50	50
Keeshond	19	18
Kerry Blue Terrier	18	15
Labrador Retriever	30.5	28
Lakeland Terrier	7.5	7
Leonberger	70	50
Lhasa Apso	6	4
Maltese	4	3
Mastiff	90	75
Newfoundland	65	55
Norfolk Terrier	6.5	6.5
Norwich Terrier	6.5	6.5
Old English Sheepdog	36.5	29.5
Papillon	2	2.5
Pekingese	6	5.5
Pointer	30	25
Pomeranian	2	2.5
Poodle, standard	24	19

Breed	Male	Female
Poodle, miniature	6	6
Pug	7	7
Pyrenean Mountain Dog	50	40
Rottweiler	55	45
Rhodesian Rigdgeback	36.5	32
Rough Collie	25	21.5
St. Bernard	80	65
Saluki	24	19
Samoyed	32	18
Schnauzer, minature	9	7.5
Schnauzer, standard	18	16
Schnauzer, giant	45.5	41
Scottish Terrier	10	9
Shar Pei	23	23
Shetland Sheepdog	9	9
Shih Tzu	6	6
Siberian Husky	24	20
Spaniel American Cocker	11	10.5
Spaniel English Springer	21.5	19
Staffordshine Bull Terrier	15	13
Tibetan Spaniel	5.5	5.5
Tibetan Terrier	9.5	9.5
Weimaraner	27	23
West Highland White Terrier	9	7
Welsh Corgi	11	10
Whippet	11	10
Yorkshire Terrier	3	2.5

Weighing your dog (and yourself).

To weigh your dog, stand on the scales yourself and note your own weight. Now take your dog in your arms and weigh again. Subtract your own weight from the combined weight.
The remainder is your dog's weight.

Checking for obesity.

THIN. Ribs and pelvic bones obviously apparent. Easily visible waist and abdominal tuck.

IDEAL. Ribs palpable without excess fat covering. Waist observed behind ribs when viewed from above. Abdomen tucked up when viewed from the side.

OBESE. Ribs not easily palpable under a heavy fat covering. Fat deposits noticeable at the back and at the base of tail. Waist barely visible or absent. No abdominal tuck, may even exhibit obvious abdominal distension.

Feeding Eukanuba.
How much and how often should you feed your dog?

FOR PUPPIES IN THEIR FIRST GROWTH STAGE

Average weight puppy	Suggested feeding amount			
	Age 6-11 weeks	Age 3-4 months	Age 5-7 months	Age 8-12 months
in kg	g/day	g/day	g/day	g/day
1 - 3	130	130	80	65
3 - 5	220	200	130	110
5 - 10	330	310	200	
10 - 15	470	445	280	
15 - 20	595			

EUKANUBA: PUPPY

FOR ADOLESCENT DOGS

Average weight puppy	Suggested feeding amount			
	Age 8-12 weeks	Age 3-4 months	Age 5-7 months	Age 8-12 months
in kg	g/day	g/day	g/day	g/day
< 5	230	215	135	115
5 - 10	345	325	210	170
10 - 15	490	460	295	240
15 - 20	615	580	370	305
20 - 25		685	440	360
25 - 35			530	440
35 - 45				530

EUKANUBA: JUNIOR

FOR ADULT DOGS WITH A NORMAL ENERGY REQUIREMENT

Average weight adult dog	Suggested feeding amount
in kg	g/day
< 5	80
5 - 10	135
10 - 15	200
15 - 20	255
20 - 25	300
25 - 35	350
35 - 45	435
45 - 55	525
55 - 65	595
65 - 80	675

EUKANUBA: REGULAR

FOR ADULT DOGS WITH A NORMAL TO HIGH ENERGY REQUIREMENT

Average weight adult dog	Suggested feeding amount
in kg	g/day
3 - 5	85
5 - 10	125
10 - 15	180
15 - 20	230
20 - 25	270
25 - 35	325
35 - 45	400
45 - 55	460
55 - 65	515
65 - 80	585

EUKANUBA: PREMIUM

the ins and outs

OF GOOD DOG CARE

You can do regular check-ups yourself.

All dogs, whether puppy or adult, should get regular check-ups to make sure all is well. You can do a great deal yourself. Once a week or so, take a good look at your dog's eyes, ears and mouth, his coat, toes and nails.

Of course, whenever you're in doubt about your dog's health, visit your veterinary surgeon.

Coat.
All dogs need regular grooming. Grooming removes dead hair, dirt and parasites. It stimulates the blood supply to the skin which will result in a healthier and shinier coat. If your dog is long haired or curly haired, you will need to take him to the groomers regularly.

Ears.
In case of excess earwax, you can help to keep his ears healthy by gently cleaning easy-to-reach areas with a moistened cotton-wool ball. Don't probe into his ear with any object. The inner ear is very vulnerable.

Eyes.
Keep his eyes clean by wiping the skin around the inner corners of his eyes gently with a clean cotton-wool ball soaked in warm water.

Stools.
Your dog's stools should be small, firm, with little odour.

Paws.
If something has to be cut out from the fur between or around your dog's paws, use blunt-tipped scissors and be very careful not to cut into the web between his toes.

Nails.
Ask your veterinary surgeon to show you how to clip your dog's nails the first time. Only use dog nail clippers, not scissors. Carefully clip a little at a time to avoid cutting the quick.

Mouth.
It is a good idea to accustom your puppy to having his teeth brushed. Be careful not to hurt his gums, or he'll be too frightened to let you, or the vet, clean his teeth.

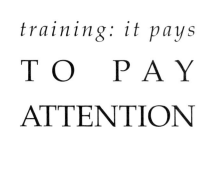

training: it pays

TO PAY
ATTENTION

Training: it pays to pay attention.

You love your dog. You feed him only the best, groom him and show him affection. But if you want him to really thrive, there is still more you must do. We're talking of training and exercise. Training is important for obvious reasons.

You have a responsibility to train your pet to be a well-behaved, disciplined member of the community. His psychological health will benefit and he will be a much more enjoyable companion if you take the time to train him properly. Exercise is essential for your dog's physical well-being.

Start with a collar and lead.

Get your puppy accustomed to a collar and lead. Start with a narrow, soft collar at first, and let him wear it constantly until he gets used to it. Then attach a light lead to the collar, long enough to reach the ground, and let him drag it around for a few days. Now the trick is to pick up the other end of the lead without starting a tug-of-war. Hold it straight up and walk along, coaxing your puppy to walk along with you. If he lags behind or runs ahead, a few short, gentle tugs are all that should ever be used. Try to stay together, so your pup won't feel the lead too much and won't start to think of it as an uncomfortable restraint.

Teaching him his name.

The best way to teach your dog his name, is by using it frequently and consistently. Say his name in a bright, animated tone that gets his attention. Do this while playing with him, when you bend down to pet him, or when you're about to put his meal bowl down. He'll soon understand that when you or anyone else says his name, he should pay attention.

Training and timing.

Your dog is really very conservative. He likes you to put him on a regular schedule, in feeding as well as training. Go for short training sessions, starting with five or ten-minute periods, gradually working up to longer sessions. Before meals is the best time. A slightly hungry dog is more alert and lively than a just-fed and ready-for-a-nap dog.

TIPS TIPS TIPS TIPS TIPS TIPS TIPS

You may have heard about phantom pregnancies: bitches whose bellies actually get bigger and bigger, without being pregnant. Often this can be due to a, real or perceived, lack of attention.

What your dog likes about you?

Your dog is authority minded by nature, so here are a few do's and don'ts for the master.

Maintain good attitude: your dog's attitude depends entirely on you, so always end training on a happy note. Both you and your dog will feel pleased.

A few examples:

Wagging his tail: *'Hello!'*.
Tail between his legs, ears down: *'I'm scared'*.
Lying on his side, one hind leg in the air: *'You're the boss'*.
Licking you: *'Love you, too'*.
Forepaws parallel to the ground, head low, tail high:

Be consistent. Use the same tone and word every time you give a certain command. If you say, 'Come Tasha!' in a bright, encouraging voice during one training session, don't switch to 'Here Tasha!' with an authoritative tone during the next. Be firm, and let your dog know training is not play.
Be patient: stop when you feel irritable.
Respond immediately: your praise or correction should always follow immediately your dog responds to a command.
Your tone of voice is of the utmost importance: praise him extravagantly, correct him with a short, stern 'No'. Physical reprimands and shouting will never help a dog. A well-trained dog will respond because he wants to please his master, not because he's afraid of him.

What you may see in your dog.

As every owner gradually discovers, his dog has a wide sounding range of barks.

From growling to whimpering, from yelping to whining, each has its own distinctive meaning. Listening to your dog, you will soon find out what he's trying to say. But your dog has other ways of expressing himself. A lot of his intentions and feelings can be seen simply from his posture.

'Let's play!' Ears high in the air: *'You don't frighten me'*.
These are but a few examples. Of course, you'll see a lot more in your own dog.

Training for competition is lots of fun.

Two examples of popular sports for dogs clearly demonstrate the fun you and your dog can have with training and competition. Flyball, a relatively new and very fast sport, is a kind of relay race over hurdles. Two teams of dogs, (normally

How does your own dog express himself? Note some of his particular sounds, postures and facial expressions.

_____
_____
_____
_____
_____
_____
_____
_____

four per team), race against each other to get the fastest time. The first dog runs over hurdles to a flyball box where he activates a pedal or similar device propelling a ball into the air which he has to catch. He then has to return with it over the same hurdles. Once he has crossed the start/finish line the next dog can set off and repeat the process.

The height of the hurdles is decided by the smallest dog, so every team tries to include a small dog.

Agility is another fun sport. Dogs race over a type of obstacle course consisting of various pieces of equipment including a see saw, weaving poles and a flexible tunnel. The course must be completed in order, and each obstacle must also be tackled in a correctly controlled manner. As the name suggests, this sport promotes one of the most valuable basics in your dog.

If you are interested in participating in one of these sports, there are official clubs you can contact who will supply details of regulations and leagues.

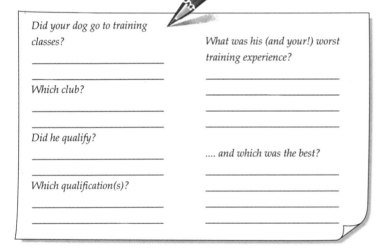

Did your dog go to training classes?

_____

_____

Which club?

_____

_____

Did he qualify?

_____

_____

Which qualification(s)?

_____

_____

What was his (and your!) worst training experience?

_____

_____

_____

.... and which was the best?

_____

_____

_____

Affix a photo in here.

Affix a photo in here.

And this is ......

Teacher's pet!

friends, all

KINDS OF
FRIENDS

Fight like cats and dogs.
Cats and dogs aren't always the best of friends.
Your dog may share your house with your cat very happily, but the saying isn't without reason.
An obstacle seems to be the misinterpretation of each other's body language.
The posture your dog uses when he wants to play, unfortunately resembles the pose your cat adopts when she's ready to attack.
It's like saying 'How do you do' in a country where these

exact sounds mean 'Do you want to fight'. In addition, the difference in size may not help either. However, as both have a very keen sense of smell, it seems your cat and dog, will accept each other quite easily when they both have the same "pack smell" - the unique and typical scent of your family, imperceptible to the human nose.

Young dogs and old dogs.
Usually, a bitch will rule over her puppies, even when they have grown up. But when two dogs from different packs come together, for example a young one and an older one, fighting can result to establish the hierarchical order. This is an inborn instinct, independent of the size of dogs, their sex or their strength. Once the authority is clear, there is peace. Try to intervene as little as possible. Only when the stronger one gets sick or injured, the power struggle might restart - and by the way, fighting does not necessarily imply bloody scenes!

Your children and your dog.
Anybody who has seen a baby and a puppy playing together will tell you - one way or another, these two understand each other. In general, children and dogs do live together very well - as long as you make sure your children do not harass your dog. For children's development the company of pets is very important.

Affix a photo in here.

Generation gap? Never heard of it!

A very special friend:

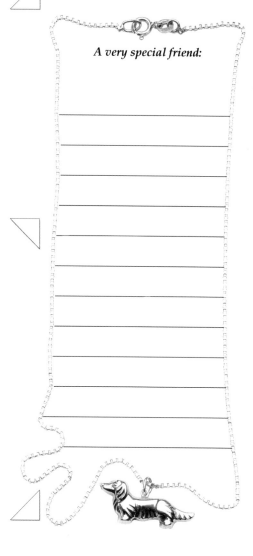

Affix a photo in here.

Friends through thick and thin.

TRAVELLING TOGETHER

Get him used to travelling.
Whether you live in a town or in the country, your dog will have to get used to travelling. At the very least, your dog should expect rides to and from the veterinary surgery for check-ups or treatment.
It is important for your dog to work up a tolerance for being in a moving vehicle, be it a car, bus or train. Get your dog accustomed to rides with a ten-minute trip every other day for a couple of weeks. Gradually increase the length of these trips.

Affix a photo in here.

My first holiday adventure.

Check where you are staying - before departure..
If you plan to stay in a hotel, motel or campsite, check ahead to ensure that pets are welcome.

Travelling Abroad
When travelling abroad,

remember each country has its own regulations regarding a dog's entrance. Most countries require at least certificates stating good health and proof of recent rabies vaccinations.

But some countries enforce quarantine legislation. Request information before travelling.

IMPORTANT:
For specific requirements of a certain country contact the Ministry of Agriculture or engage the services of professional exporter. If you are planning to return to the UK, your dog will have to undertake the statutory six months quarantine.

TIPS TIPS TIPS TIPS TIPS TIPS TIPS TIPS TIPS TIPS TIPS TIPS TIPS TIPS TIPS TIP s

Don't drive your dog immediately after he's eaten, especially if he's prone to car sickness. 🐾

Go for a short walk with your dog before departure. 🐾

If your dog is used to a certain box, cage or travelling pen, by all means take it with you if it's manageable. Take along his

favourite toy or blanket. 🐾

When travelling by car, keep it well ventilated. Don't let your dog hang his head out of the window: he could easily get a bug or piece of sharp grit in his eyes or nose. 🐾

Stop regularly at a parking area to let your dog out for a drink of water, some exercise, and to relieve

himself. Keep him on a lead while he's in a strange place. 🐾

Do not leave your dog in the car on hot days. Dogs can suffer from heat stroke very quickly - it can be fatal. 🐾

what's so special about

THE IAMS
COMPANY

In the unique Animal Care Centre - pets are paramount.
The Iams Company is no ordinary pet food manufacturer. Ever since its foundation nearly fifty years ago, the Company has had a single purpose: we want to be the best in creating superior food for your pet.

To establish this superiority, we operate our unique Animal Care Centre in the U.S.A. where cats and dogs of many breeds are observed in a home-like environment. A lot of time is spent playing with the pets and coaching them.

We determine their nutritional needs in different life stages and life styles and we spend many animal test days before we accept a new product. In some cases even up to 49,000 pet test days!

Why Eukanuba is the best you can do for your dog.
Eukanuba is a complete, meat-based diet containing a highly palatable formula of animal proteins, animal fats, vitamins, minerals and carbohydrates. It's highly digestible, so your dog obtains more usable nutrition from every gram. Benefits? Small, firm stools with little odour and excellent skin and coat condition. You'll see healthy skin and a glossy coat after about six to eight weeks, and after several months sound muscle tone.

Feeding your puppy Eukanuba from the start, will ensure his teeth and bones get everything they need for perfect growth

Look at the ingredients and their balance.
All Eukanuba dry foods, (apart from Lamb and Rice which contains real lamb meat), are made with chicken and egg,

two of the purest, most digestible sources of protein. We insist on nothing less than the very best ingredients from the same trusted suppliers, regardless of raw material prices or availability. Which is why every bag of Eukanuba is always of the same consistent high quality.

We never use fillers, binders, artificial colours, flavours, or preservatives.

The Eukanuba Range.

Eukanuba is available in bags and in cans. There are six products in the dry range to fit in with every dog's age and lifestyle. Eukanuba is also available in cans for adult dogs. When you want to reward your dog, there are nutritious Eukanuba biscuits.

EUKANUBA PUPPY.

A complete, balanced high-nutrition food for young dogs, specially formulated to meet the very special needs of a growing puppy. It's an excellent weaning food.

EUKANUBA JUNIOR.

A complete, balanced food designed to meet the special nutritional needs of the adolescent puppy, particularly if you've got one of the larger breeds.

EUKANUBA REGULAR.

A complete, balanced food providing an excellent maintenance diet for adult dogs with a normal level of activity.

EUKANUBA PREMIUM.

A complete, balanced high-quality food providing optimum nutrition for dogs with normal to high activity levels. It's ideal for pet dogs, show dogs, working dogs and during pregnancy and lactation.

EUKANUBA LIGHT.

A complete, balanced food providing all the nutrients needed by an adult dog if he has a below-average level of activity or a tendency to be overweight.

EUKANUBA LAMB & RICE.

A complete, balanced quality food for your dog, prepared with fresh lamb meat. Especially appropriate for dogs suffering from poor skin or coat conditions.

EUKANUBA BISCUITS.

A tasty and nutritious treat, made with the highest quality ingredients. The perfect complement to Eukanuba food, and ideal when you want to reward your dog.

Eukanuba products are available at pet shops, veterinary surgeries, kennels, garden centres and other specialist pet food outlets.

Further information .

The Iams Company's sole purpose is enhancing the well-being of cats and dogs through world class quality foods. We are genuinely concerned about your dog's well-being, so if you have any questions about feeding your dog, don't hesitate to contact nutritionists at the address below. We'll be pleased to help you.

**Leander International Pet Foods Limited,
Arden Grange,
London Road,
Albourne, Hassocks,
West Sussex, BN6 9BJ.
Tel: 01273 833390
Sole importers to the UK and Ireland.**

Iams Pet Food International, Inc., Airport Office Center, Luchthavenweg 67, 5657 EA Eindhoven, The Netherlands.